VIOLIN

Fifty Elementary Studies

ROWSBY WOOF

The Associated Board of
the Royal Schools of Music

£4.95

ELEMENTARY STUDIES

ROWSBY WOOF

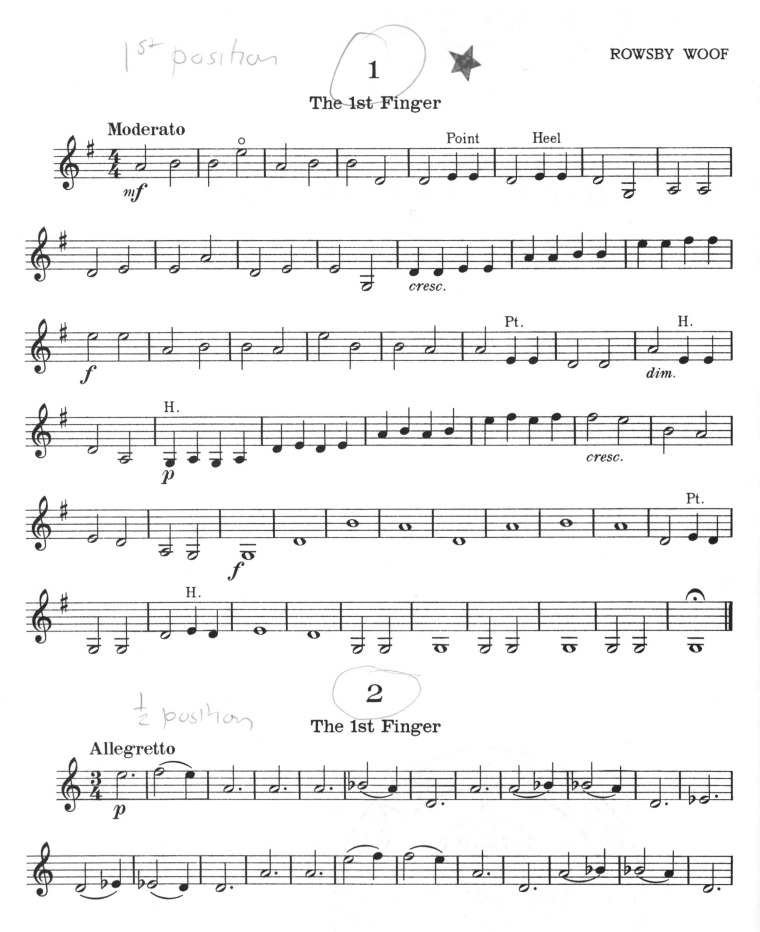

3

1st and 2nd Fingers

4

4

1st and 2nd Fingers

5

1st and 2nd Fingers

6

The 1st Finger on Two Strings
Should be played as smoothly as possible

7

1st and 3rd Fingers

Tempo di Valse

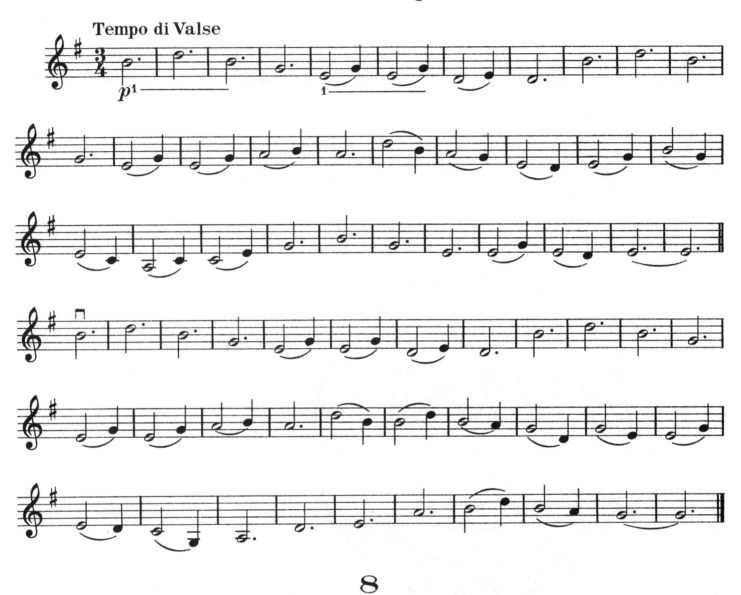

8

1st and 3rd Fingers

Allegro

9

2nd and 3rd Fingers

10

Semitones between 2nd and 3rd Fingers

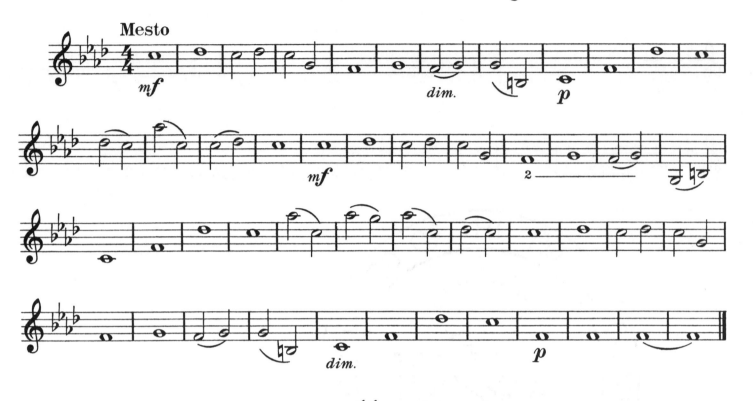

11

2nd Finger on Two Strings

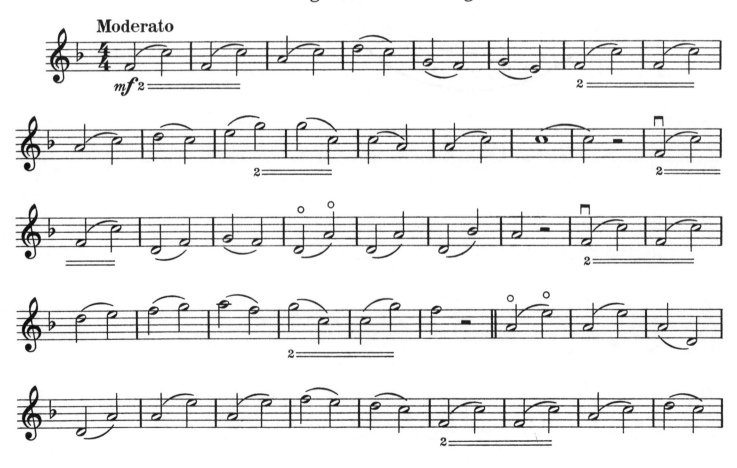

12

Semitones between 1st and 2nd Fingers, with use of 3rd also

13

1st, 2nd and 3rd Fingers

14

1st, 2nd and 3rd Fingers

15

1st, 2nd and 3rd Fingers

16

1st, 2nd and 3rd Fingers

17

Preparatory Exercise for Trills
Lift the 1st Finger high

18

Preparatory Exercise for Trills

Lift the 2nd Finger high

19
Preparatory Exercise for Trills
Lift the 3rd Finger high

20

Preparatory Exercise for Trills

Lift the upper Finger high

21
Arpeggio Exercise

22
Arpeggio Exercise

May also be practised:—

23

Arpeggio Exercise

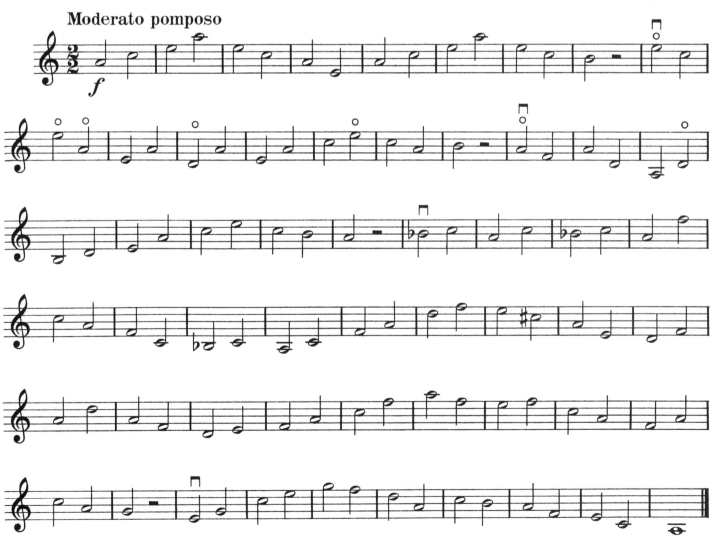

24
Arpeggio Exercise

25
Arpeggio Exercise
With occasional use of the 4th Finger

26

Preparatory Exercise for Grace Notes

27

Preparatory Exercise for Grace Notes

28

The 4th Finger

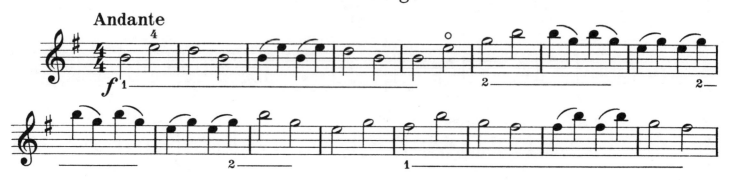

29

The 4th Finger

30

The 4th Finger

31

The 4th Finger

32

Scale Passages without 4th Finger

33

Scale Passages without 4th Finger

34

Scale Passages without 4th Finger

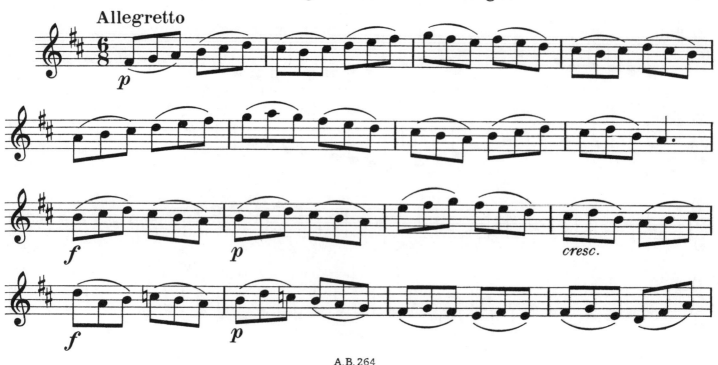

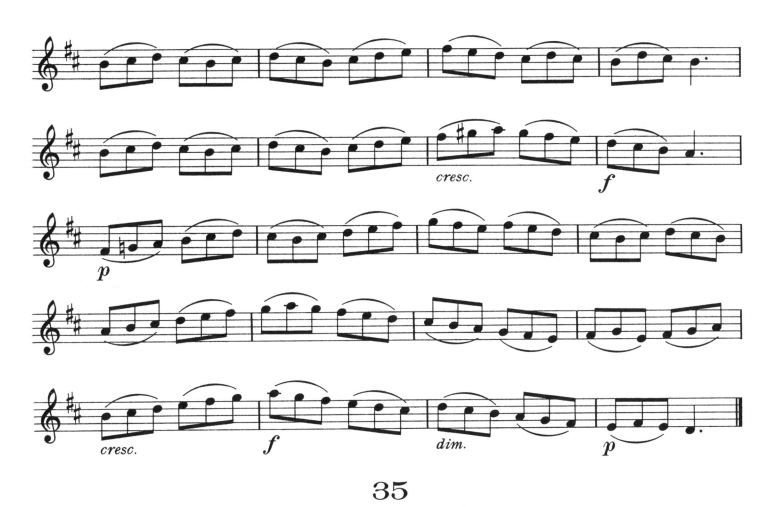

35

Scale Passages without 4th Finger

36

Scale Passages without 4th Finger

37

Scale Passages without 4th Finger

38

Scale Passages without 4th Finger

39

Scale Passages without 4th Finger

Should also be practised:—

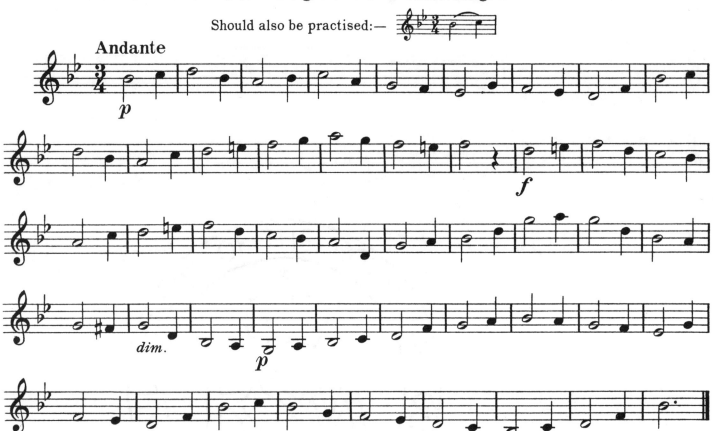

40

Bowing Exercise for Legato Crossing of Strings

41

Bowing Exercise for Legato Crossing of Strings

42

Bowing Exercise for Legato Crossing of Strings

43

Bowing Exercise for Legato Crossing of Strings

44

Exercise for Lifting the Bow

Should be played near the Heel. About one third of the bow should be used. The bow should travel quickly and lightly along the string for each up or down-bow stroke.

45

Exercise for Lifting the Bow

Should be played near the Heel. About one third of bow should be used. No "break" or lift should occur between the up-bow and down-bow strokes.

46

Exercise for Lifting the Bow

Should be played near the Heel. Lift the bow only where the rests are. Make the bow travel freely.

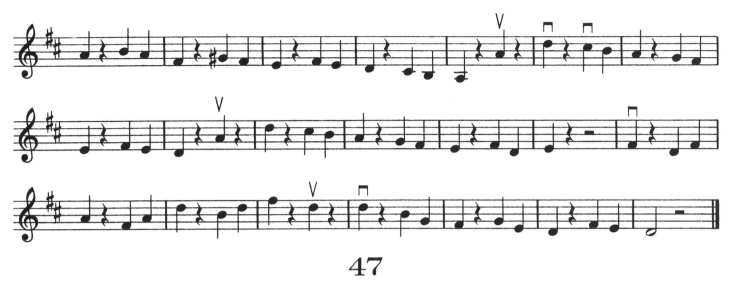

47

Exercise for Lifting the Bow

Use as much bow for single up-bow note as for the two slurred in down-bow. Lift the bow for the rests only.

A.B. 264

48

Arpeggio Exercise
To include the 4th Finger

49

Arpeggio Exercise
To include the 4th Finger

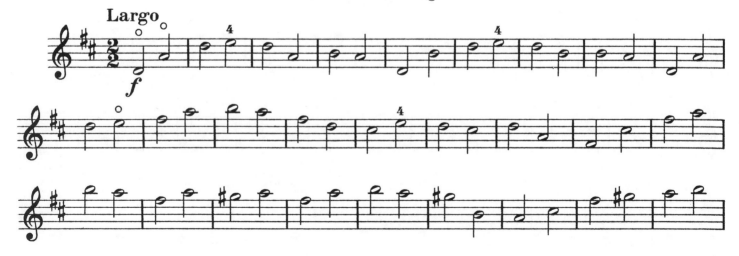

50

Arpeggio Exercise
To include the 4th Finger

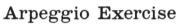

Printed in England by Caligraving Limited Thetford Norfolk

A.B. 264

4:06